THE JOURNEY OF
ODYSSEUS

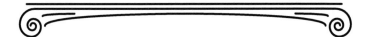

FOLLOW YOUR FATES SERIES

The *Follow Your Fates* series enlists you the reader as the main character in the classic literature of ancient Greece and Rome. You assume the identity of each character, follow his story, and make the decisions he makes. Each decision you make will determine whether or not you continue to follow your fate, or whether your fate will quickly come to an end. Make the right choices, and you too can complete the quests of the greatest heroes of the ancient world.

Each *Follow Your Fates* story adheres to the story of its ancient counterpart. If you successfully follow your fate, you will experience firsthand the story of the ancient original. For instance, in order to complete the full story of *The Wrath of Achilles*, you must make the decisions that Achilles makes. But do not expect these decisions to be obvious or logical. Many of these decisions in fact might seem wrong or uncomfortable by today's standards. You may find yourself making decisions that you don't agree with so that you can continue to follow your fate. These differences, however, provide an important opportunity for comparison and are the unique aspect of this series: in a more traditional format you the reader remain detached from the character and analyze his decisions objectively; you are not invested in those decisions in any way. In the *Follow Your Fates* series you yourself are making these decisions; you are forced to analyze your own motivations and reasoning. You should consider what made you make your decision and what might have made the character make his decision. In this way, you will learn not only about the ancient world and its values but also about yourself and your values.

Finally, have fun. My goal for this series is simple: to introduce readers to the literature, history, and mythology of the ancient world in an engaging, enjoyable way. Ancient literature is some of the most important in the world if for no other reason than that it has lasted so long. The reason it has lasted so long? Readers of every age and type have found something of value in it and have done so for over 2,000 years. Will the books written today last so long? We'll just have to wait and see. Until then, enjoy the classics of ancient Greece and Rome.

THE JOURNEY OF
ODYSSEUS

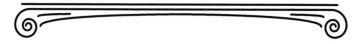

BY

ED DEHORATIUS

ILLUSTRATED BY

BRIAN DELANDRO HARDISON

Bolchazy-Carducci Publishers, Inc.
Mundelein, Illinois USA

Editor: Laurie Haight Keenan
Contributing Editor: Andrew Reinhard
Cover Design & Typography: Adam Phillip Velez
Illustrations: Brian Delandro Hardison

The Journey of Odysseus

Ed DeHoratius

Bolchazy-Carducci Publishers, Inc.
1570 Baskin Road
Mundelein, Illinois 60060
www.bolchazy.com

Printed in the United States of America
2010
by Publishers Graphics

ISBN 978-0-86516-710-0

For my Dad, my first and best teacher.

Acknowledgments

First and foremost, I need to thank Christine Rhodes, Wayland High School class of 2003, whose *Choose Your Own Adventure* senior project on the Black Death showed me the potential of marrying that format with academic material and ultimately inspired the *Follow Your Fates* series. The students of the Wayland High School classes of 2007 and 2008 who took my Classical Literature class read early drafts of *The Wrath of Achilles* and provided suggestions about the text and encouragement to continue with the project. Andrew Reinhard of Bolchazy-Carducci was instrumental in bringing this project to fruition and Laurie Haight Keenan of Bolchazy-Carducci was an invaluable resource on all things editorial. Lou and Marie Bolchazy too deserve great thanks not only for their continued support and promotion of the classics but also for their willingness to experiment and take risks. As always, my family, Liz, Will, Matt, and Andrew, my parents, and the Kennedys, have shown infinite patience as I continue to write.

INTRODUCTION

Ten years at war, surrounded by fellow soldiers, arming, fighting, wounding, killing. For ten years, it is all you have known. And now it is over. Now it is time to go home. Home is quiet, peaceful, pleasant. There are no enemy soldiers waiting around the corners of buildings, there are no enemy arrows whizzing past your ear, there are no enemy swords clanging even in your dreams, long after the fighting has stopped. And you're pretty sure you will miss, in some twisted way, every single aspect of war. Sure, you want to see your wife Penelope and your son Telemachus, but you wonder how easy it will be to become husband and father again when you have been warrior for so long.

You are the great Greek warrior Odysseus. Your story was told by the Greek poet Homer in the epic poem the *Odyssey*. You reluctantly left your island home of Ithaca, located off of the coast of northwestern Greece, for the Trojan War, leaving behind your loving wife and your young son. But once embroiled in the war at Troy you became one of Greece's most famous warriors, both for your prowess in battle and the cunning of your mind. In fact, it was you who conceived of the ruse that finally brought about the fall of Troy: the

Trojan Horse. Secretly holding Greek warriors in its hollow belly, the huge wooden horse was left outside of the gates of Troy supposedly as an offering to Athena. The Trojans foolishly brought the horse into their city and that night, while the Trojans celebrated, the Greeks emerged and began the destruction of the city.

That destruction is over and now you must journey home. Yours will be a long and arduous journey, but make the choices that Odysseus makes in Homer's *Odyssey* and you will follow your fate to a successful completion. Good luck!

THE JOURNEY OF ODYSSEUS

The day you have dreaded has arrived. You look to the horizon from your beautiful island of Ithaca and see a lone Greek warship approaching. It moors in the harbor, but you already know who it is and what they want.

Years ago, when all of the Greek princes were desperate to make the beautiful Helen their wife, you, one of these princes, approached Helen's father with a suggestion. In exchange for Helen's cousin Penelope, you proposed that all of Helen's suitors make a pact: that whoever does not marry her swears to protect her. Even as the broker of the deal, you too made the pact. Now you realize that the approaching ship means that you will be expected to honor the oath that you made. Something has happened to Helen.

Continue to the next page.

A servant brings swift word from the harbor: "Palamedes comes to you as the envoy of General Agamemnon. Helen has been kidnapped by the hateful Trojan Paris. It is time to honor your oath. The Greek army assembles at Aulis."

You have a choice to make.

If you agree to go with Palamedes to Aulis, turn to page 23.

If you refuse him outright, turn to page 46.

If you attempt to trick him into thinking you can't go with him, turn to page 37.

You quickly recover yourself after the horror of the sudden death of your comrade; you have spent the last ten years fighting mighty Hector and the Trojans. You quickly look to your men; they recognize the look in your eye and signal that they're behind you. No one can so brazenly disrespect the Greeks, Cyclops or not.

You are the first to reach Cyclops with your sword drawn, and tragically only now do you realize how overmatched you are; you are hardly as tall as the Cyclops' knee. You plunge your sword into the only place you can reach, but realize how futile your attack will prove. You manage a brief thought of Penelope and Telemachus as the Cyclops' huge hand comes toward you, and you realize that this, unfortunately, is . . .

THE END

You decide that you have what you want, your freedom and your life, and that it's best to not to further risk your men's lives; you remain silent. When Cyclops' island is completely out of sight, you finally breathe a sigh of relief, feeling safe for the first time since you arrived there.

As you turn away from the side of the ship, you notice an unfamiliar look in your men's eyes. They face you, and one speaks: "Mighty Odysseus, when we sailed with you to Troy, we sailed with you for glory and for honor. When we left Troy, we left with glory and with honor. Now we leave Cyclops' island, having defeated and outsmarted an enemy perhaps greater than any we faced at Troy. But where is our glory? According to Cyclops, 'no one' defeated him. According to Cyclops, 'no one' blinded him. Where is the glory and honor in that?" Your men silently return to the business of sailing. Although you remain their leader and captain, you have lost their respect. They never look at you or listen to you the same again. The choice to remain silent, for you, was . . .

THE END

Your horror overcomes your grief; you have a ship full of men to protect and a family at home waiting for you. It pains you to make the decision, but this is why you are the captain of the ship. You tell the men to load up the ship and shove off. You wonder if you saw something flicker in your men's eyes, but you dismiss it as simple fatigue or relief at having survived yet another brush with death.

As you settle behind the wheel, Circe's land shrinking behind you, a group of men approach you: "We can't leave them behind. If you don't take us back, we'll swim back and take our chances." You slowly nod your head; their courage and resolve shame you. You turn the ship around, not knowing whether you will survive your return to Circe's palace.

But that no longer matters. You've lost the trust and faith of your men. Whatever happens, for you, this is . . .

THE END

Polyphemus bellows in anger, but resolves that he will not be defeated. To your astonishment, he removes the huge boulder from the entryway; your escape route lies open! To your disappointment, however, he proceeds to fill the opening with his huge body, blocking any way of escape. He will wait to catch you where he knows you must go, even if he can no longer see you with his lone eye.

You have a choice to make.

If you choose to take Polyphemus by surprise and rush the doorway immediately, turn to page 16.

If you choose to wait for an opportunity for escape to present itself, turn to page 35.

The gods continue to smile on you. You gladly take Hermes' protective potion from him and bang on the door of Circe's palace. She admits you immediately, as if she expected you.

You demand that your men be restored to their human form. She smiles and agrees: "Of course, Odysseus. I know you and your reputation. I would never cross you. But first, sit, eat. You have been on a long journey and need your strength."

Softened by Circe's openness, you sit as she piles the food before you. You eat eagerly; she watches you eat, as if expecting something to happen. You continue to eat, knowing that Hermes' potion is working. Finally, you speak.

Continue to the next page.

"Circe, I am immune to your powers, and I demand that you return my men to their human form. The gods ordain this."

Circe hangs her head. "Hermes told me you would come. Hermes prophesied this, and I have no choice but to comply. Go. Return to your ship to fetch your other men. Bring them here so that we can all feast together. When you return, the men that were turned to pigs will be restored. I swear it to be true."

Joyfully, you deliver the news to your men and return to Circe's palace. Indeed, you eat and drink with Circe and your men. In fact, you eat and drink so much, the days turn into weeks, the weeks into months, and the months into a full year. You seem not to have noticed how much time has passed, but your men have. They approach you, urging you to return to the sea. You have a choice to make.

If you choose to continue to stay with Circe, turn to page 50.

If you choose to listen to your men and leave Circe, turn to page 36.

8

Your love for Penelope and Telemachus is too strong; you cannot take any more time away from your journey home. And can the gods really fault you for putting your family first? Disappointed but excited, you turn the prow of your ship toward home.

Your journey home is uneventful. Perhaps too uneventful, but you push such negative thoughts from your mind as the craggy shore of Ithaca finally appears on the horizon. You have made it home! You can't wait to embrace your wife and son.

But your excitement is short lived, for, as if out of nowhere, dark clouds appear before you. Thunder crashes and lightning flashes. Your ship rises and falls with the huge swells. Finally, the inevitable: a single wave swamps the ship, sending it, you, and your men into the sea.

You wonder how you will get home, until the ghostly face of your companion Elpenor appears to you. You realize now that you should have buried him; respect for the dead and the gods is important above all else.

THE END

You realize immediately that you cannot trust the Cyclops. Revealing your name to him would allow him power over you that you are not willing to give him. Thinking quickly, you instead invent a ruse that will soon save your life.

"Cyclops. I am happy to reveal to you who I am as a sign of our growing friendship. They call me 'No one.' That is the name I go by. Now let us continue with our feast. More wine, my new friend."

The Cyclops drinks more and more wine, until he can no longer hold up his immense head. He is fast asleep.

Your plan continues to work. But after the next step, there will be no turning back. Your fate, good or bad, will be sealed.

Turn to page 31.

1. You are Odysseus, one of the premier warriors who fought at Troy. The Cyclops will prove a formidable opponent, but you will not shrink from a battle with him.

2. You are wily Odysseus, the inventor of the ruse of the Trojan Horse. The wit of the Cyclops is no match for yours; you can trick him into letting you leave.

3. You are patient Odysseus. Ten years at Troy, always missing Penelope and Telemachus, has taught you the value of patience. Another day or two to ensure your return seems a simple sacrifice.

If you choose to attack the Cyclops, turn to page 3.

If you choose to trick the Cyclops, turn to page 17.

If you choose to wait for your opportunity to escape, turn to page 86.

11

You are mighty Odysseus, Greek warrior, son of Laertes, prince of the island of Ithaca, sacker of Troy, and Cyclops needs to know who defeated him. You did not achieve your current status by being humble.

"Polyphemus! I am Odysseus, son of Laertes, ruler of the island of Ithaca, sacker of Troy. It is I who blinded you, I whom you knew as 'no one.' Take solace, though. You have been defeated by one of Greece's greatest warriors."

Your men stare at you in horror. What does it serve to taunt Polyphemus? But before they can even wonder, you and they are engulfed in sea water from the splash of a huge rock thrown by Polyphemus. You laugh out loud. "Throw as many rocks as you like, Polyphemus. They will not restore the sight that I, Odysseus, took from you."

Indeed, Polyphemus threw no more rocks, but instead simply prayed: "Poseidon, my father, god of the seas, I pray you to avenge me on Odysseus, son of Laertes, ruler of the island of Ithaca, sacker of Troy. If he must return home, let him return alone and battered. Curse his journey and torture him and his companions."

Continue to the next page.

You leave Polyphemus flush with pride at your successful ruse and escape. Little do you know what awaits you because of that pride.

But you sail on, stopping next at the island of Aeolus, the god of the winds. He takes pity on you and your plight and gives you a sack filled with all of the winds, so that they can't blow you off course, but he reveals the contents of the sack only to you.

His blessing works; you arrive in the waters off the coast of Ithaca quickly and swiftly: you can see your people on the island and smell the familiar scent of your home. This is what lingers with you as your eyes grow heavy with sleep. You have remained awake to ensure that no mistakes were made, but now sleep can no longer be resisted. You should have rested on the journey; you won't be this close to home again for a long time.

Continue to the next page.

You will later learn that your men thought that you had been hiding riches from them, that the sack from Aeolus contained gems and jewels that they wanted for themselves. When they opened the sack, all of the winds were released, and you were blown hopelessly off course and away from your island home of Ithaca.

You return to Aeolus with the hope of placating him and perhaps garnering a second chance, but Aeolus wisely recognizes the influence of a god more powerful than he; he commands you to leave him immediately.

Your woes continue at your next stop. Hoping to find friends in the Land of the Lastrygonians, instead the huge king tears one of your men limb from limb and serves him for dinner. When you attempt to flee, he hurls rocks at your ships. Every ship is destroyed but yours; you mourn your lost comrades, but can't mourn for long.

Continue to the next page.

You next arrive at the land of Circe, a sorceress famed for her magic powers, but remain at your ships to recover from your harrowing journey. After refreshing yourself for two days on your stored food and a stag the gods sent to you, you decide that it is time to investigate. You will contact Circe to determine if she is friendly and to sec if she can help you.

How you proceed, however, will prove essential to your survival.

You have a choice to make.

---

*If you choose to lead the expedition yourself,
turn to page 47.*

*If you choose to send an expedition of your men out to
investigate and report to you, turn to page 22.*

The moment is now. Polyphemus is reeling from his wound, and you realize that he is at his most vulnerable; if you don't act now, you may never be able to.

You and your men charge the doorway and Polyphemus' huge body, knowing that you must find any opening that presents itself to escape.

But as you get closer to him, you realize just how big he is and just how much of the doorway he blocks. As you reach the doorway, you scatter for the few spaces that are not blocked by Polyphemus. But there are so few spaces and so many of you that you clumsily run into one another before you can even reach those spaces. Polyphemus, hearing the commotion below, only has to reach out his big hand and scoop you up in groups of two and three.

You don't even have time to think of your wife and young son as you feel yourself being brought to Polyphemus' mouth. The only thing you can think is that this is . . .

THE END

Your problem is not only the Cyclops, but also the huge boulder that he uses to block the door; you and a thousand men could never budge it. When the Cyclops leaves that day to pasture his sheep, you formulate your plan.

Your eyes fall to his huge club. With some work, you can use it to your advantage. You and your men cut it down to size, smooth the sides, and sharpen the tip to a sharp point; you fire the tip to make it rock hard, and you hide it in the cave.

When the Cyclops returns, you welcome him heartily, even after he thoughtlessly eats two more of your men (you choke back your horror and grief; you must remain strong if the plan is to work).

"Cyclops, learn the quality of Greek wine. Wash down your meal with a gift from us."

The Cyclops finishes the wine in one gulp and demands more. Your plan is working.

Continue to the next page.

As the Cyclops drinks, his tongue loosens. He begins to view you more as a guest than as his next meal. "Stranger, guest in my cave, who are you who brings such wondrous drink from so far away? I am Polyphemus, son of the god of the seas Poseidon. Tell me your name so that I can repay you with a gift of my own."

You continue to ply the Cyclops with wine, as you ponder his request.

You have a choice to make.

If you choose to reveal your name to the Cyclops in the hopes of placating him, turn to page 30.

If you choose to hide your name from the Cyclops because you still don't trust him, turn to page 10.

"Odysseus did this to me. The great Greek hero Odysseus, son of Laertes, ruler of the island of Ithaca, he has blinded me." As you hear the lumbering thuds of the Cyclopes approaching Polyphemus' cave from all over the island, you immediately realize your mistake; your men too realize your mistake.

You tacitly agree, however, that you cannot wait for the Cyclopes to arrive. If you will die, you will die fighting. Immediately, you all draw your swords and rush headlong towards Polyphemus and the door of his cave that he is blocking.

In the chaos of battle, as you see companion after companion fall to the Cyclops, your final thought is of your wife and son. If only your wit had not failed you this one time, you might have made it home after all, and this would not be . . .

THE END

"Each of Scylla's six heads snatches a man from the deck."

You will risk the danger you can see. Scylla's six heads at least can be attacked and defended; what can you do against a raging cone of water?

Despite Circe's warnings to the contrary, you don your armor and prepare for battle. But you have barely grabbed your shield and sword when Scylla's six heads each snatches a man from the deck. You see your men struggling, and you hear them calling out to you. And then: silence and stillness. They were some of your best men, and you grieve for them, but your grief cannot last; you have passed Scylla and have survived. Your journey can continue.

Turn to page 29.

You and your men agree that you will draw lots to see who will investigate; Eurylochus draws the short straw.

You don't have to wait long for his return. Breathlessly, he arrives but cannot speak; you can read the horror on his face. Finally, he describes what happened.

"We gained entrance to the palace. Everyone sat down at Circe's table, but I sensed a trap and did not eat. As the others ate, I saw it happen before my eyes. One moment, they were men. The next, they were pigs. She used her powers to change them into pigs! I ran until I came back here."

Horrified and grief-stricken at the same time, you realize that you have a choice to make.

If you choose to cut your losses and leave Circe's land immediately, turn to page 5.

If you choose to go to Circe's palace yourself to recover your men, turn to page 51.

You hang your head at the prospect of leaving. You turn to see your wife Penelope and your infant son Telemachus, knowing that it will be years, even decades, before you see them again. You will miss the entirety of your son's youth for the foolishness of some Trojan boy.

But you also recognize your commitment to Helen and Greece and cannot shirk that duty. You hug your wife, kiss your son, and with a heavy heart head to the harbor to meet Palamedes.

That night, in a deep sleep, the goddess Athena appears to you. She is your patron goddess; she looks after you, she takes care of you. She now speaks to you in your dreams.

Continue to the next page.

"Odysseus, my favorite, what have you done? You leave your loving wife and infant son without a thought? You leave them without even an attempt to stay home? I expected more from you, from wily Odysseus. I expected more from the man that I have protected and advised all these years. You may continue on to Troy. You may fight in the battles, and you may even emerge victorious. But you will do so without my aid. Farewell, Odysseus. This will be my last visit to you."

You wake up to the rise and fall of the ship on the swells. Calmly in the moment between being asleep and awake, you recall Athena's message. You realize then that, whatever glory you may accrue at Troy, you have lost your divine protection; your life will never be as blessed as it was. For you, the battle has ended before it has even begun.

THE END

Reluctantly you realize that Circe knows something that you don't; she delivers words from the gods, and such words cannot be ignored.

You sail beyond the bounds of the known world, beyond the Pillars of Hercules that mark the western boundary of the Mediterranean. You perform the required rituals, and the ghosts of the dead appear before you.

First is your companion Elpenor, who was with you in Circe's land. Surprised, you wonder how he arrived here before you. He explains that he accidentally fell to his death from Circe's roof. Worse, though, his body remains unburied, and he implores you not to continue your journey until you bury his body.

Continue to the next page.

Next, you see your own mother, and you immediately feel your eyes moisten with tears; when you left for Troy, she was still among the living. How did she end up here? She approaches you, and you move to embrace her, but you pause because you also see Teiresias approaching. You need to speak with Teiresias, but you want to speak with your mother. You have a choice to make.

If you choose to speak to your mother, turn to page 88.

If you choose to speak to Teiresias, turn to page 66.

Your men are tired and hungry, and you realize that they could use a rest, but your instinct as king of Ithaca and warrior at Troy tells you that you should move on to a safer locale.

You break the news to your men that you will continue on. And although they detested you at the time, they are thrilled with you now: you all have arrived home in Ithaca! You quickly bid your men farewell and rush home to your wife and son.

Penelope is both shocked and excited to see you. She throws her arms around you, and you hug for what seems like forever. Telemachus arrives and, although you hardly recognize him after ten years, his appearance and his bearing mark him unmistakably as your son. You too embrace. You feast all night, as you look forward to your future together as a family.

Continue to the next page.

Those first few days with Penelope and Telemachus are magical; you can't believe that you are back home in Ithaca after fighting for so long at Troy.

But soon, something changes. You start to miss Troy. You miss the camaraderie, the danger, the thrill. Life around you in Ithaca is, well, boring. There is nothing to do. Yet even with nothing to do, you still feel nervous all the time, as if a Trojan warrior could attack you from every doorway, sword drawn, menace in his eyes.

Your time at home is difficult. You and Penelope are fighting. You and Telemachus are fighting. Even you and your father Laertes are fighting. You find yourself spending more and more time away from home, until one day you find yourself at the dock. What is most remarkable, however, is that you are not alone. Most of your men are there too.

Wordlessly you all board your ships and set sail. You know not where you are going, but you know that you can no longer stay home. As much as you wanted to get home, you now realize that you are not yet ready to be home.

THE END

Having survived Scylla and Charybdis, you see on the horizon the island home of the sun god Helius. Circe warned you about this island, and your heart fills with dread at the impending danger.

"Companions, I know that you are tired and spent from our quest, but we must continue on our journey. Grave danger awaits us here on this island."

The faces of your companions fall, and Eurylochus addresses you on their behalf. "Mighty Odysseus, you ask too much. We are tired and hungry and tossed about by the violent sea. You should give us rest here on this island so we can recover for the rest of our journey."

You have a choice to make.

If you choose to listen to Eurylochus and give your men a rest on the island of the sun god, turn to page 65.

If you choose not to listen to Eurylochus and continue on your journey past the island of the sun god, turn to page 32.

You smile at your good fortune; Athena remains with you. "Good Cyclops," you reply, "I thank you for your hospitality. I am Odysseus, son of Laertes, ruler of the island of Ithaca. I will be happy to accept whatever gift you are able to give to me. To toast our new friendship, let us continue to drink this fine wine that I have brought with me."

The Cyclops drinks more and more wine, until he can no longer hold up his immense head. He is fast asleep.

Your plan continues to work. But after the next step, there will be no turning back. Your fate, good or bad, will be sealed.

Continue to the next page.

You allow the Cyclops to sleep a bit to ensure that he is in as deep a sleep as possible. You and your men then uncover your sharpened club and hold it over the fire until it is white hot. You briefly confer with your men; you have one chance to do this, and mistakes will prove deadly.

Working together, you all hoist the sharpened point over your head and run full speed at the Cyclops, plunging the club straight into his lone eye.

He lets loose a bellow of pain that shakes the entire island. His fellow Cyclopes, hearing him, immediately call out to him from all over the island: "Polyphemus, what is happening? Why do you shriek in pain? Who has done this to you?"

If you told the Cyclops your name,
turn to page 19.

If you did not tell the Cyclops your name,
turn to page 96.

Eurylochus has a point. But the danger is too great to risk stopping. You know your men are tired and hungry, but avoiding the short-term risk of stopping at Helius' island will prove beneficial in the long term. You quietly but firmly break the news to your men that you are continuing on.

An eerie silence falls over the men. They do not sulk, they do not scream. Rather they hold your gaze for what seems like a moment too long. Then they turn to Eurylochus, who remains silent.

You realize that the men are upset, but they will have to get over their disappointment if they ever hope to return home. You turn away and resume the business of captaining the ship.

Continue to the next page.

You feel an imperceptible movement of the air behind you. When you turn, you find yourself nose to nose with Eurylochus: "Odysseus, we have traveled across every land with you. We have risked our lives and been put into unnecessary danger by your foolishness. Yet you won't even allow us to rest our bodies and grieve our lost companions. I am here to tell you that you are no longer in command of the ship. The men are with me now. You can peacefully relinquish control of the ship to me, or you can resist us."

You have a choice to make.

If you choose to relinquish control of the ship peacefully to Eurylochus, turn to page 81.

If you choose to resist Eurylochus' takeover, turn to page 91.

"You cling to the underbelly of one of Polyphemus'
sheep and ride it to freedom."

You, wily Odysseus, cannot be outsmarted by the Cyclops. As you listen to his bellowing, you hear another sound: the bleating of his flock of sheep. You have your answer, which you quickly explain to your men.

As day breaks, Polyphemus beckons his fleet to pasture without leaving the doorway. As he lets them pass, he feels them all around to ensure that you are not among them. But he does not feel their underbellies. There you and your men cling, your backs perilously close to the ground, your faces buried in soft fleece, hoping as you pass that his large paws do not reach around and discover your ruse. But they do not. You ride his flock to freedom.

Turn to page 82.

You realize that your men are correct. You have been with Circe too long, and it is time to travel home. When you tell her your decision, however, her response surprises you: "Odysseus, you should not stay here any longer than you want to; I certainly do not intend to keep you beyond your will. But you cannot yet resume your journey home. Rather, you must make a stop on the way. You must journey to the land of the dead to speak with the blind seer Teiresias. He will help you reach home successfully."

Your heart breaks, your men shout in protest. All you want to do is head home. You have a choice to make.

If you heed Circe's words and journey to the underworld, turn to page 25.

If you choose to go straight home to Ithaca, turn to page 75.

You realize immediately that you cannot ignore the oath that you made. If Palamedes demands you, then you must accompany him. But perhaps there is another way . . .

You quickly and quietly whisper something to the servant. When Palamedes finds you, he sees not the mighty Greek hero whom he expected, but rather a man smeared with dirt, whose disheveled hair indicates not a prince of Greece but rather a madman.

You, of course, are the same Odysseus you have always been, but if you can convince Palamedes that you are not mentally fit to go to Troy, perhaps he will leave without you.

You are on the beach with your plow. You have yoked it to a horse instead of an ox. And you plow that beach as if preparing to plant crops.

Turn to page 39.

"Palamedes places your infant son Telemachus
in front of the horse and plow."

But as you rage behind your plow, doing your best to convince Palamedes that you are better left home, something catches your eye, something in Palamedes' arms . . . Your heart stops as you realize that it is not some*thing* in his arms but rather some*one*. He has your infant son Telemachus with him, as he wordlessly approaches you; his eyes never leave your face.

You catch Palamedes' eye for a split second when perhaps you recognize his understanding of the situation. But you have no time to reflect on that. Palamedes has placed your infant son in front of the horse and plow. You have a choice to make.

If you choose to stop the horse and admit your deception, turn to page 89.

If you choose to call Palamedes' bluff and continue with your plowing, turn to page 77.

For nine days you drift on your raft. On the tenth you find yourself beached on an island. You shudder, recalling the dangers you faced on other islands.

Suddenly, a beautiful woman appears before you. She smiles and opens her arms to you. "I am Calypso. Welcome. I will not harm you, and I will feed and clothe you. Come."

She is a stranger, a woman who may or may not be trustworthy. You have a choice to make.

If you choose to trust Calypso and go with her, turn to page 52.

If you choose to decline Calypso's offer and go it on your own, turn to page 71.

The next morning, another stranger appears in the doorway of Eumaeus' hut. But this one apparently is only a stranger to you; Eumaeus' dogs recognize him. It is your son. It is Telemachus. He has returned safe from a long journey to inquire after you, despite the suitors' desire to kill him upon his return. He asks Eumaeus to go to the palace to tell Penelope of his safe return. You and your son, whom you've waited to behold for so long, are alone in the swineherd's hut. You have a choice to make.

If you choose to take this opportunity to reveal yourself to Telemachus, turn to page 99.

If you maintain your disguise and wait to reveal yourself to Telemachus, turn to page 92.

41

Perhaps you realize that you should stay with Circe, but your yearning to see Penelope and Telemachus overrides your common sense. You politely decline Circe's offer and continue on your journey home.

After a few days at sea, a strange but beautiful sound begins to wash over the boat. It gets louder and louder until you recognize it: female singing. With horror, you realize that you are sailing past the Sirens, women famous for luring sailors with their enchanting voice.

With urgency, you encourage your men to keep rowing, to stay on course, but it is too late. They have already turned the ship toward the sound, and you tragically realize that it is too late.

The last sound you hear is the horrific crash of the hull of your ship against the rocks. The last thought you have is that, perhaps if you had rested with Circe for one more day, this wouldn't be . . .

THE END

You decide to take your chances with the whirlpool. You can navigate around a whirlpool more easily than you can battle a six-headed monster.

You immediately pace up and down the deck, exhorting your men to pull their oars harder than they ever have. If you are to avoid Charybdis, you must have speed and pinpoint control over your ship.

You continue to encourage them, even as you yourself catch a glimpse of the vast expanse of empty water that is Charybdis; you hope your voice doesn't betray your concern.

Continue to the next page.

You quickly realize that there is no escaping Charybdis. She is too large and too powerful. You continue encouraging your men, but understand, as your ship first gets caught in the slope of Charybdis' trough, that you will not survive her.

Your men soon realize that they no longer are controlling the ship; it is caught in the vortex of Charybdis. Some of them panic. Some of them remain calm. All of them, however, including you, realize that this is . . .

THE END

Your throat filled with water, you clutch desperately to a scrap of wood left over from your once proud ship. You alone have survived. But you wonder for how long.

As the winds change, however, the current takes you along the route you've already traveled, which will ultimately return you to Scylla and Charybdis. You shudder to imagine how you can survive them with just a raft, when you barely survived them with a sturdy ship.

Turn to page 55.

You rush toward the harbor and meet Palamedes on his way to your palace. You stare him square in the eye; he understands without you even having to speak. Indeed, he speaks first: "Odysseus, if you choose not to accompany me, if you choose not to honor the oath that you took, you will be no more an ally to the Greeks than the Trojans are." You say nothing, but continue to hold Palamedes' gaze. He grasps your intentions and continues: "No more can be done now; the Greek forces are assembling, and we cannot afford to waste any more time here. But rest assured, however long our siege of Troy lasts, when it has ended, you will again see Greek sails on the horizon. And when we arrive, we will not be nearly as cordial as we are now. Goodbye, Odysseus. We will meet again."

You watch Palamedes sail away and then turn to your wife Penelope and your infant son Telemachus. You take solace in the fact that you will see him grow, but you shudder to think that you will not live to see him reach manhood.

THE END

It is only right that you yourself should lead the group to investigate this new locale.

You and your men come through the woods to face a palace of finished stone on a hill. In the grounds around the palace are wild beasts of every sort but, rather than attack you, they approach you and sniff you, as if wanting to tell you something.

As you approach the door of the palace, you hear singing inside, and immediately a desire to see this woman seizes you. She welcomes you to her palace, sits you and your men at her table and feeds you well.

Too well. Something is not right.

You feel your nose thickening, your ears elongating. Your body bends to the ground and becomes thicker, heavier. You see your fingers and toes join together to form hooves. You have a sudden need to bathe yourself in mud. You are a pig.

Circe's potions have done you and your men in. You now understand that the beasts in the courtyard were really men like you trapped in the bodies of beasts.

You don't know what will happen to your brain, but you do understand at least that this is . . .

THE END

"As you beg food from the suitors to test their honor,
one of them hits you with a stool."

You wait and finally enter the palace. Telemachus ensures that you receive some food, and Athena tells you to go to all of the suitors to beg food from them as a test of their honor. One of them, Antinous, mocks you, and when you threaten him with revenge, he hits you with a stool. You bear the blow silently, but the commotion that it causes reaches Penelope.

Eumaeus approaches: Penelope has requested a meeting with her new guest, the stranger. You suggest that you meet that night; a meeting in view of the suitors might cause undue attention. Remember, she has no idea that it is you.

Turn to page 95.

You dismiss your men offhandedly. You are enjoying yourself too much and you happily return to your food and drink.

Time continues to pass, so much time, in fact, that you don't even realize how much. Your food- and drink-addled brain, however, pauses long enough to notice that Circe's palace is much less crowded than it used to be. "They left. They all left," she tells you. "They could not stand the waiting anymore and voted to leave you here. You are all mine now."

You should be stunned; you should be insulted, angry, offended. Surprisingly, however, you are not. You have been here so long, have eaten and drunk so much, that your emotions have dulled beyond recognition; why shouldn't they have left you? As you turn back to your plate and goblet, you realize for one moment before you resume consuming that, as for your journey home and your old life, this is . . .

THE END

Your face steels with resolve. You will not leave your men to be disgraced by Circe's magic. At your look, your men rise and join you, all except Eurylochus, who remains too afraid to return.

On your way to the palace, a young man in a winged helmet and sandals appears suddenly before you. You immediately recognize him as Hermes, the messenger of the gods.

"Odysseus, son of Laertes, ruler of Ithaca, sacker of Troy, are you so foolish to think that you can defeat Circe's magic and recover your men without assistance? You will fail and be trapped forever like them, unless you accept my assistance. This potion will protect you against Circe's magic. Take it and be successful."

You feel comforted by Hermes' words and begin to reach for the vial, but pause. What if he and Circe, two divine beings, are working together? You have a choice to make.

If you choose to accept Hermes' help and potion,
turn to page 7.

If you are suspicious of Hermes and feel more
comfortable approaching Circe on your own,
turn to page 56.

"Calypso, your offer is very generous, and I thank you for it. I am happy to accept any assistance that is offered me."

Calypso takes you to her palace where for seven years you live like a king. You eat and you drink to your heart's content; whatever you want is yours.

One day she presents you with an offer: "Mighty Odysseus, sacker of Troy, stay with me. Stay with me forever. I offer you what few mortals have been offered: immortality. You can stay with me and be treated like a god. Be my husband and live the way you deserve to live."

You have a choice to make.

If you choose to accept Calypso's offer and stay with her forever, turn to page 80.

If you choose to decline Calypso's offer and continue home, turn to page 69.

You boil with anger at the insolence of a lowlife like Melanthius, but know that you must keep your emotions in check. He will get his in the end.

You and Eumaeus arrive at the palace. You hear the playing of the lyre from inside and the rowdy commotion of the feasting suitors. Again, you seethe with anger, but you maintain your disguise before Eumaeus. "This must be great Odysseus' palace," you proclaim innocently.

"Indeed," responds Eumaeus. "Wait outside while I go in; hopefully you will not attract attention and insults from others."

Turn to page 49.

You depart weary from Troy, but stop to refresh yourself on a nearby island. There you sack and plunder the city, but when you encourage your men to depart, they stay and continue to celebrate. While they dawdle, the remaining islanders arm themselves and attack. You lose six men from each ship in the ensuing battle.

Your next stop takes you to the Land of the Lotus-Eaters. You send a group of three men out to investigate who lives here, but they never return to the ship. You send another group out, and they never return. Finally, you venture out on your own, only to discover your men blissfully unaware of how much time has passed. You, however, shock them back to reality, force them to the ships, and quickly leave before any other men become ensnared.

Next, you spot an island that appears deserted: no crops, no towns, no ships. Your men could use a rest, but the desolation of the island worries you. You have a choice to make.

If you choose to stop and rest your men, continue to page 60.

If you choose to heed your foreboding and sail on, turn to page 27.

The crash and roar of Charybdis signal that you have indeed returned. Desperately trying not to panic before the prospect of certain death, you try to peer through the waves and water for anything to help you through.

The gods have not entirely deserted you! You spot the branch of a fig tree extending into the water. Just as you feel your raft being sucked into the vortex of Charybdis, you grab the branch and hang there. You now just have to wait for your raft to be spit back out of Charybdis and hope that it is before your arms give out. Indeed, just as your hands start to slip from the branch, you see your raft. You swing from the branch and land on the raft, floating to safety.

Now you just wish you knew to what danger the current will lead you next.

Turn to page 40.

You smile at Hermes' ruse, but you are wily Odysseus and cannot be fooled by such simplistic attempts. You push past Hermes and bang on the door to Circe's palace. She admits you immediately, as if she expected you.

You demand that your men be restored to their human form. She smiles and agrees: "Of course, Odysseus. I know you and your reputation. I would never cross you. But first, sit, eat. You have been on a long journey and need your strength."

Softened by Circe's openness, you sit as she piles the food before you. You eat eagerly; in fact, your appetite seems to be growing. You can't seem to stop yourself from eating.

It is then that you catch your reflection in the 'wine' that Circe has served you. Your head is no longer human. Your ears are longer, your nose stouter: you are a pig, just like the rest of your men, and trapped here forever. Hermes was right: without his help, this is . . .

THE END

You awaken alone on land with the Phaeacians no-where in sight. Where have they abandoned you? Have they kept their promise to you? Is this Ithaca?

You see a young boy on the beach, whom you ap-proach. He soon reveals himself to be the goddess Athena in disguise. She confirms that indeed this is Ithaca (you are finally home!), but tells you that suit-ors have taken over your palace and harry your wife Penelope. Athena disguises you as an old beggar so that you might move among them unrecognized. You thank Athena; if it weren't for her, you might have ended up as the Greek general Agamemnon did, killed unceremoniously upon his return home. You must proceed with care.

Continue to the next page.

In disguise and briefed by Athena on the situation in the palace, you know exactly where to go. You find your loyal swineherd Eumaeus in his hut. You maintain your disguise and do not yet reveal yourself, but are pleased that Eumaeus expresses his distress over your absence and treats you, a guest, well; the same apparently cannot be said for the suitors and their treatment of your home and your wife Penelope.

After a lavish meal for which Eumaeus kills his fattest hog, you sleep, content that Eumaeus has remained loyal to you over all these years.

Turn to page 41.

You quickly and purposefully stride toward her; when you reach her, you fling yourself on the ground and wrap her legs with your burly arms.

But before you can begin to speak, she screams. Her friends, already having run away upon seeing you emerge, run more quickly and begin screaming themselves. The combined noise of all of the women screaming quickly brings the men from the town, and when they see you wrapped around the legs of their princess, they don't wait to ask questions.

Their swords are immediately drawn, and they pounce upon you. Your protests go unheard; in fact, the only thing that is heard is your screaming. For you, this is . . .

THE END

Despite your misgivings, the needs of your men come first. Besides, after ten years at war, what could you possibly face here that is worse than the mighty Hector and his Trojan warriors?

After you and your men have rested, you, with twelve of your best men, explore the island. You come upon a cave with a huge opening, and you venture inside. Spying some cheese, you all eat your fill and await the inhabitant's return, hoping that he will be reverent and hospitable.

How wrong you were!

Continue to the next page.

An immense beast of a man (if you can call him that) practically fills the huge opening of the cave when he returns. He brings his goats into the cave, where he milks them, leaving the male goats outside; half of the milk he sets aside for cheese.

When he lights his fire, he spies you and your men. As he sees you, you too see him more clearly. Atop his huge shoulders, in the middle of his forehead, sits a single, lone eye: a Cyclops. You shudder in fear, realizing that you are not in a place where the laws of man apply.

Turn to page 93.

However much you desire to resume your journey home, you understand the importance of Circe's offer. You and your men accept her offer of sustenance.

Over dinner that night, Circe explains to you the difficulties you will face on the rest of your journey, and, more important, she tells you how to avoid may of the pitfalls that await you. Emboldened by her advice, you depart the next morning, refreshed and ready to face what lies ahead.

Continue to the next page.

Your first test is the island of the Sirens, beautiful women who lure sailors to their doom with their entrancing song. As Circe instructed, you plug your men's ears with beeswax; you, however, ever curious, lash yourself to the mast with your ears free: you can hear the Sirens' song but are prevented from hurling yourself in the water to follow them.

As you pass the island and you come under the spell of the Sirens' song, you thrash against the rope and yell to your men to set you free. Your men, however, as instructed, only tie you tighter until the song of the Sirens is no longer audible.

But you have accomplished what few men have: you have heard the Sirens'song and lived to tell about it.

Continue to the next page.

Next you approach a violent strait between two cliffs. This pass will prove perhaps more dangerous even than Polyphemus the Cyclops, for on one side lies Scylla, the six-headed sea monster who with her long necks can pluck men from the deck of their ship, and on the other lies Charybdis, a swirling whirlpool that, if navigated incorrectly, can swallow your entire ship into the depths forever.

You cannot continue your journey without encountering either Scylla or Charybdis; the strait is too narrow to avoid them both. You have a choice to make.

If you choose to sail closer to Scylla and risk her six heads, turn to page 21.

If you choose to sail closer to Charybdis and risk her whirlpool, turn to page 43.

Reluctantly you agree. While you fear what may happen on the island of the sun god, you recognize that Eurylochus is correct, and it is important to maintain the morale of the men on a journey as long as yours.

You, however, leave specific instructions with your men: no matter what happens, the cattle of the sun god are not to be eaten. The men agree.

For thirty days, contrary winds prevent you from leaving. For thirty days, you eat the stores on your ship. But after the thirty days, your food runs out, and the men take to hunting on the island.

Concerned, you strike inland to pray to the gods for safe passage home. While away, the combination of fatigue from your journey from Troy and your trek inland force you to give in to a deep sleep.

Turn to page 87.

However much you yearn to speak to and embrace your mother, you understand the importance of speaking to Teiresias. You cannot let your emotions override your purpose.

Teiresias approaches, and you speak. Immediately, you understand the importance of talking to Teiresias and that the dangers of the journey to the land of the dead pale in comparison to the dangers you would have faced without having spoken to him.

When he falls silent, a quiet confidence overtakes you. You now know what you have to do to return home safely. If the gods remain by your side, perhaps you will one day see your wife and son again.

Continue to the next page.

After Teiresias departs, you see other shades from your past. The mighty Ajax, because of your dispute over Achilles' armor, marches past in silence; he still cannot forgive you.

But Agamemnon, the leader of the Greek forces against Troy, describes his bloody homecoming, how his wife Clytemnestra and her lover Aegisthus murdered him in cold blood, in the bathtub.

And Achilles, greatest of all the Greek warriors, looking ashen and sullen, describes the loneliness of the underworld: "I would rather live as the lowest servant to a sheep herder than rule over all the souls of the dead." All of the glory Achilles garnered on earth means nothing to him or anyone else now that he is dead.

Continue to the next page.

But your time is short, and the dead begin pressing around you. You worry that they will take you with them, and you will not be able to escape. Quickly, you urge your men to push off and return to the seas and your journey.

The first soul to whom you spoke, your helmsman Elpenor, asked you to return to Circe's land to collect his body before resuming your journey home.

He is your comrade and friend, and you should abide by his wishes. But you have a long way to go and have already spent a long time diverted from your journey.

You have a choice to make.

*If you choose to return to Circe's land
to bury Elpenor, turn to page 72.*

*If you choose to resume your journey home
immediately without burying Elpenor,
turn to page 9.*

"Calypso, it is difficult for any mortal to resist a woman as beautiful as you. The chance to spend eternity with you is one difficult to pass up. But pass it up I must. I am in love with my wife. I have a son. My father is at home. I mean no offense, but these things are all more important to me than immortality. I hope you can understand."

Calypso smiles and nods. "The god Hermes has already appeared to me: Zeus demands that I release you and send you on your way. So you may go, Odysseus. You may return home to your wife and your son. Farewell."

Continue to the next page.

You build a raft. You set sail. You have sailed for days when Poseidon finds you and continues your torment, still angry about your blinding of his son Polyphemus. A huge storm dashes your raft and leads you to an unknown island. You wash ashore naked and bleeding. You hope the inhabitants are friendly. But before you can worry too much, you fall into a deep sleep.

You awaken to the sounds of splashing water and shouting girls. You emerge, covering yourself as best you can with a branch. Before you stands a beautiful young woman. You have a choice to make.

———————————————

If you choose to fling yourself at her feet, begging for mercy, turn to page 59.

If you choose to hold back and address her from afar, turn to page 97.

You have trusted too much on this journey home, and where has it landed you? Companionless, shipless, naked, and wet on an unknown island. "Lovely Calypso," you begin, "while your offer is more than generous, I will catch my breath here on the beach and resume my journey."

Calypso's eyes darken like the storm that brought you to her island. "Do you know who I am?!" she bellows. "How dare you insult a goddess?! You, Odysseus, will pay! Not with your life. No. That would be too easy. But you will remain here with me on this island forever. Every day you will awaken and remember your wife and son at home, and every day you will remember that you will never see them again."

Your heart breaks at Calypso's words. Whether you escape, and she kills you, or you stay here forever, for you, this is . . .

THE END

With resignation and determination, you return to Circe's land. The gods and the dead must be respected, however much you desire to resume your journey home. Circe is not surprised to see you, as you complete Elpenor's burial rites.

"Odysseus, your journey to the land of the dead was difficult and tiring. Stay an extra day here. I will feed you and care for you so that you may regain your strength."

You yearn to return home, but you realize that Circe speaks the truth. You have a choice to make.

If you choose to stay with Circe and let her take care of you, turn to page 62.

If you choose to politely decline Circe's offer and resume your journey home, turn to page 42.

Your friend Mentor appears, but you recognize that it is Athena in disguise. She encourages you and gives you strength. The suitors' spears miss their mark, and you recognize Athena's hand behind it.

Finally, it is done. Bodies surround you. One is alive, the bard, he who performed for the suitors at dinner. He approaches on his knees and begs for mercy. Telemachus vouches for him, and you allow him to live.

There is grisly work to be done. You call the nurse Euryclea and tell her to summon the women who were disloyal to you while you were gone. They clean the mess and then are killed for their betrayal. Finally, you order Euryclea to bring you fire and sulfur for a final fumigation of the house. There will remain no evidence of the slaughter.

It is time to see Penelope.

Continue to the next page.

Euryclea summons Penelope with the good news. Penelope doesn't believe her. Even when Penelope sees you sitting there, she cannot bring herself to believe that it is you. Telemachus reproaches her, wondering how she can keep herself from you. But you quiet him: "Your mother has been through a great ordeal. Let her test me to her satisfaction."

Penelope eyes you. She looks you up and down. Indeed, she recognizes you, but she must be certain. "Euryclea, we have had a hard day. Bring my bed out of the very room that Odysseus built. Cover it with blankets to keep the stranger warm for the night."

This is your test. You have a choice to make, perhaps the most important one of your life.

If you choose to remain calm and accept Penelope's invitation to sleep as a stranger, turn to page 106.

If you choose to grow angry at Penelope's doubting of you, turn to page 101.

You hear Circe's words but refuse to listen. You and your men are too tired and too eager to return home. You thank Circe repeatedly for her kindness and her concern, but assure her that you and your men will be fine. She watches you leave, and you wonder if you see the glint of a tear on her cheek.

Continue to the next page.

The rest of your journey home is uneventful. You moor at Ithaca soon after leaving and excitedly send a messenger ahead to the palace to announce your arrival.

As you proudly approach your home, it strikes you as perhaps odd that Telemachus and Penelope have not greeted you; hadn't they received the message of your arrival? But no matter. You realize that your sudden and unexpected return has surprised them and that they are unprepared for your return home.

When you open the door and enter, a sight strikes your eyes that you were never prepared to see. Young men surround Penelope and feasts of food she has set out. But before you can react, you feel the warm sensation of iron piercing your flesh. You don't know who has stabbed you, but you do know that this is ...

THE END

You are mighty Odysseus and will not be intimidated by Palamedes. You set your jaw and plow on.

What happens next is a blur. You see the look of horror on Palamedes' face. You can't tell whether he's more horrified for you or himself. You hear someone screaming, until you realize that it is you. Your only thought now is what you will tell Penelope.

In a moment of morbid clarity you realize that your obstinacy killed your son. Your life as you know it is over. Whether you go to Troy or just go away, you know that you will never return to Ithaca again. How can you face Penelope? What would you say? How could you explain yourself? Your arrogance and pride has made this moment ...

THE END

Penelope emerges, inspired by Athena, and announces to the suitors a contest. The winner of the contest, she pledges, will take her as a bride from this palace she has called home. She sets up twelve axes, with leather loops on the bottom of the handles, in a row, and she presents the mighty bow of her husband Odysseus. "Whoever can string Odysseus' bow and shoot an arrow through the loops of all twelve axes will have me as his bride."

The suitors are excited; finally, their opportunity to prove their prowess and win your Penelope for themselves. But your heart races too, for a different reason. You realize that this is the time not only to reveal yourself but also to punish the suitors once and for all.

Each suitor confidently approaches the bow. Each suitor departs dejected, unable to bend Odysseus' mighty bow.

Turn to page 85.

You wheel on Melanthius. "Dirt? How dare you insult your king that way?" And immediately the staff that was once supporting your frail body becomes the weapon that is beating Melanthius for his insult. But, unaccustomed to your older body, you cannot fight as effectively, and Melanthius, bleeding and injured, is able to get away.

You see everyone staring at you, and soon you hear a commotion from the palace. A group of men, swords and shields in hand, approaches. The suitors. No matter. You are Odysseus, sacker of Troy. But your older body again betrays you, and soon you are overwhelmed by the suitors. As they plunge their swords into you, you wonder if that is Penelope you see behind them. Perhaps a single glimpse of her somehow can comfort you for your fatal mistake. Either way, for you, this is . . .

THE END

How can you resist such an offer? You, Odysseus, who is always curious and always striving, can now experience what few mortals have: an immortal life with a beautiful goddess.

Calypso beams at your acceptance and immediately leads you to the table, overflowing with food and wine. You look forward to such opulence forever.

But you quickly discover that there is more to life than food and drink. However much she feeds you, you still feel empty. You miss Penelope. You miss Telemachus. You miss your mortal life. You realize that immortality removes the very aspect of life that makes it worth living: its finality. Without the inevitability of death constantly looming, all else loses its importance.

You know now with horror that you will spend an eternity wishing that you had chosen to return home to your son, to your wife, to your mortal life.

THE END

You quickly realize that there are too many of them and only one of you; resisting will only lead to needless violence and harm. You bow your head as a sign of submission.

Eurylochus himself leads you below deck. "You will remain here for the remainder of the journey. When we return to Ithaca, your palace and your riches will become ours. We will give you some land in the country to live out the rest of your years with your family. But as mighty warrior and captain of this ship, for you this is . . .

THE END."

Finally out of Cyclops' cave, you head directly for your ships and immediately set sail. As you watch Cyclops' island recede in the distance, you still feel alive and electric, like you did after a day of battling at Troy: an intoxicating combination of fear, uncertainty, and arrogance. You are pleased that you have not yet lost the edge that being at war for ten years gave you.

In battle, glory is based on your enemy's knowledge of his conqueror. But the Cyclops does not know your name; you will accrue no glory from this victory. You begin to gloat to him, even from this far away, about your victory, but check your impulse; you are no longer on the battlefields of Troy. You have a choice to make.

If you choose to gloat to the Cyclops about his defeat, turn to page 12.

If you choose not to gloat and remain silent, turn to page 4.

You hate to think it, but there are too many of them and not enough of you. If it were you alone, you would risk it and relish the opportunity to die in such a battle. But your son is by your side, and the loyal swineherd. It is for them that you lay your sword down.

"Suitors, I acknowledge your superior numbers and sue for peace. This is what I propose: you all put your swords down and leave with your lives. I leave my sword down and resume my rightful place as lord of this land." The suitors reluctantly agree, and you settle into your life as ruler, reunited with your family.

But after a few months, you become listless; this is not the life for you. The suitors look at you differently; they have lost respect for you. Finally, exasperated, you leave the island in Telemachus' hands and depart to seek further adventure. You find it, perhaps, but you don't even know what you're looking for. What you do know is that for you, mighty Odysseus, this is . . .

THE END

"You announce that you, Odysseus, have returned by
stringing another arrow and killing Antinous."

You speak up, asking for an attempt yourself. Your request is met with laughter and derision, but loyal Eumaeus begins carrying the bow to you. Serious concerns are voiced about even the possibility of a beggar such as you having the chance to wed Penelope, but she and Telemachus defend your right to try; Eumaeus finishes his long walk across the room to deliver your bow.

Effortlessly you string the bow and shoot the lone arrow straight and true through the loops of the axe handles. The suitors are astonished, but you have no time to waste. Signaling Telemachus to prepare himself for battle, you announce that Odysseus has returned, as you string another arrow and immediately kill Antinous, the leader of the suitors. The suitors howl in naive complaint, and Eurymachus comes forward, trying to placate you, asking for mercy.

You have a choice to make.

If you choose to accept Eurymachus' apology and show mercy to the suitors, turn to page 103.

If you choose to ignore Eurymachus' apology and show no mercy, turn to page 105.

What is a couple of days after ten years at Troy? Surely the Cyclops will soften toward you; then you can negotiate and broker your safe departure.

That day, two more of your men are eaten. That evening, two more. The next day, two more. And so it continues. Finally, you alone remain. The Cyclops trains his lone eye on you menacingly. You shudder as you see his huge hand reach toward you. He raises you to his grotesque face and speaks: "Foolish man, I have eaten all of your companions, and only you remain. You seem important, however, and perhaps even heroic, so I will have mercy on you by giving you a choice: would you rather I eat you as I ate your companions, or would you rather remain here alive and enslaved to me?"

But for you, this is no choice. You know now that your journey home is over, whatever you choose. Whether you become Cyclops' snack or slave, for you, this is . . .

THE END

Refreshed, you return to your men only to be horrified at what you see: the carcasses of the cattle of the sun god lay strewn about. Your men have done exactly what you told them not to do. You worry about what punishment awaits you but you must continue your journey. The next day, more favorable winds appear, and you return to the sea.

Once the fateful island of the sun god is out of sight, a great storm arises; you fear that this is not a coincidence. Indeed, the storm begins to batter your ship: the main mast is shattered and, falling, kills the helmsman. Lightning flashes, until one hits the ship directly. Everyone is pitched into the sea, your men floating next to the charred hull; none of them will make it home to Ithaca. You wonder how you will.

Turn to page 45.

You understand the importance of speaking to Teiresias, but this is your mother; he can wait. You and your mother approach. You try to hug her three times, but each time your arms only pass through her. You speak of your home, Ithaca, and your father, Laertes, who has not dealt well with your absence; he lives alone now in his country house, rarely venturing to the palace. Although your heart breaks for both your mother and your father, it is reassured at having spoken to her. Now for Teiresias.

You peer around, trying to find him, but cannot. You call out to him. He does not respond. You wait. You call out again. You wait some more. You call out again. Still, he does not appear. Finally, you depart, concerned that you did not speak to him, but comforted that you saw and spoke with your mother.

Hopefully, Teiresias' wisdom was not essential to your journey home.

Turn to page 76.

You realize that your deception has been discovered. You would never sacrifice your son's life, and Palamedes knows this. You stop the horse and rush to embrace Telemachus. With his head on your shoulder, you peer at Palamedes. You both know what this means. You slowly hand Telemachus to Penelope and go with Palamedes. You will leave immediately for Aulis to join the assembling Greek forces and then continue to Troy. Only the gods know when you will see your home, your wife, your son again. You pray to Athena that you come home from Troy safely and swiftly.

Continue to the next page.

The Trojan War lasts ten years. You emerge as one of its premier warriors. You are trusted enough for the general Agamemnon to include you in the envoy to Achilles, Greece's greatest warrior who removed himself from the war after being insulted by Agamemnon. And you came up with the idea for the Trojan Horse, the famous ruse that sealed Troy's fate and allowed the Greeks finally to take the city.

Now that the war has ended, you look forward to returning to your island home of Ithaca. Imagine how big Telemachus must be! And you yearn to see your wife Penelope again.

As you finally board your ship for the journey home, you still feel some of the adrenalin of the war coursing through your system. It's understandable after spending so much time in battle, but with Troy behind you, you must prepare yourself to reenter society.

Turn to page 54.

The insolence of Eurylochus and your men shocks you. You are mighty Odysseus, sacker of Troy. They will not intimidate you, and they will not defeat you. You meet Eurylochus' gaze with a look that says you will not go down easily. Eurylochus understands this and lunges for you, his sword drawn. You, however, anticipate his attack and have your sword ready; Eurylochus falls dead at your feet.

But before you can rejoice in your triumph, you feel hands grabbing at every part of your body. Eurylochus' death has only angered the rest of the men, and there are too many of them to fight alone. You don't know which you felt first: your body leaving the ground as the men lifted you to the side of the boat, or the pain of their swords piercing your side.

You don't need to feel the cool water of the Mediterranean closing around you to know that this is . . .

THE END

You have learned that patience is essential to success. However much you might want to embrace your son and tell him that you are home, you know that revealing yourself too early can put both you and him in danger. You sit and talk with him, maintaining your disguise.

Suddenly, Telemachus stands and delivers a curt goodbye. You see him grab his sword and shield and head for the palace. You try to follow, but your disguise hampers your progress; old beggars can't move as quickly as young warriors. By the time you get to the palace, you are horrified by what you see. Telemachus lies dead on the palace floor, and you can do nothing about it. The suitors turn to you: "Welcome, stranger. We are now in charge. If you are foolish enough to resist us, this," pointing to Telemachus, "is what will happen."

Your heart breaks as you view your dead son's body. All of the tricks, all of the danger, all for what? To lose your son, your heir? You turn and leave, a broken man. You briefly consider Penelope, but know that you are no longer capable of being her husband. You may be still be alive, but Odysseus, the great Greek warrior, is dead.

THE END

"What strangers are you who appear in my cave and eat my food? Identify yourselves!"

Even you, mighty Odysseus, are terrified, but manage to speak with some confidence in your voice: "We are Greeks, on our way home from Troy; we fought under the command of Agamemnon. We seek shelter and hospitality as the laws of the gods dictate."

The Cyclops smiles and promptly scoops one of your men into his giant hand, throws him into his mouth, and eats him whole; the man didn't even have time to scream. "The laws of the gods? Ha! They do not apply to me. You have just witnessed my law!" Horrified at both the loss of your man and your miscalculation of the Cyclops, you ponder your next move.

If you have one.

Turn to page 11 to assess your options.

You and Penelope—she so familiar to you, you only a stranger to her—talk for hours. She explains what her life has been like without you, how she deceived the suitors with the ruse of Laertes' death shroud: she promised that she would choose a suitor to marry once she had completed the shroud in which your father, Laertes, would be buried. All day she would weave. All night she would unweave, thus postponing her choice. But after three years, she was discovered, and she had to choose.

She then asks you again about yourself. You tell her the same story you told Eumaeus, one full of lies but one that protects your identity. You assure her, however, that you have heard that Odysseus will return soon. She doesn't believe you, but thanks you for your kindness. In return, she calls her maid Euryclea over and tells her to wash your feet.

Turn to page 104.

The rest of the day is tension filled. Another beggar appears and challenges you; you beat him but spare his life. You anger another suitor, prompting another stool thrown your way; this one at least misses. Finally, Telemachus authoritatively orders the suitors home for the night. Immediately you and he finalize plans for the suitors' slaughter.

You order him to take away your weapons for cleaning; they are displayed on the walls of the dining hall. If the suitors ask, he should say that the weapons have been hidden for their own protection; with all that wine flowing, weapons would only lead to disaster.

The commotion attracts Penelope's attention, and finally she is before you. Her first question: "Who are you?"

You have a choice to make.

If you choose to reveal yourself to Penelope,
turn to page 108.

If you choose to maintain your disguise,
turn to page 94.

You smile when you hear the Cyclopes' questions and Polyphemus' response: "No one did this to me! No one has hurt me!" You hear the other Cylcopes laugh as they return to their respective caves: "Well, if no one hurt you, why should we help you? Don't drink so much wine next time." You hear the Cyclopes laugh again and realize that you are safe. For now. The Cyclops' friends won't be a problem, but that huge boulder still stands in your way; until Polyphemus removes it, you are stuck in his cave, playing a dangerous waiting game.

Turn to page 6.

You understand how you would appear to a stranger; discretion is the better course: "Beautiful maiden, I know not whether you are mortal or goddess. I am shipwrecked on your island and ask for mercy and assistance. I leave myself in your care."

"Stranger, you have landed on friendly shores. Fate smiled upon you when she brought you here. We Phaeacians take care of strangers and travelers. I will help you. But, we cannot go into town together. I, a princess, being seen with a stranger, will be seen as scandalous. So wait in the woods until you think we have arrived and then come to town yourself. Ask for the king's palace, and we will take care of you there."

Continue to the next page.

You do as you are told and present yourself to the king, who welcomes you warmly and openly. He assures you of your passage home, but first you stay and feast. A herald sings songs of Troy that break your heart to hear. You participate in games and contests of physical prowess. You are presented with gifts. And finally, mercifully, you are bathed and cleaned, for the first time since you left Calypso's island.

You reenter the king's great hall a new man. A bard continues to sing songs of Troy, and you weep openly. The king notices and asks you to tell your own tale. You agree and tell him about all of your trials.

When your story ends, the Phaeacians load a ship with treasure and set off with you for Ithaca. You immediately fall asleep, hoping that they will do as promised, hoping that you will awaken with your homeland of Ithaca within sight.

Turn to page 57.

The goddess Athena appears to you and only you; Telemachus cannot see her. "Odysseus, now is the time. Reveal yourself to your son." She strips your disguise away. Your body becomes young again; Telemachus even thinks you're a god.

"Telemachus, my son. I have returned. After twenty years, I have returned from Troy. Before you stands your father, Odysseus. We will be a family again."

Telemachus cannot restrain his emotions. He throws his arms around your neck and weeps as if you had died. You look at him. Your son. Grown after twenty years away.

You want to catch up; you want to hear all about him and his life, but work remains to be done. You both sit and plot how to rid your house of the suitors.

Continue to the next page.

You both agree that your true identity will remain hidden from Eumaeus and that Telemachus will go to the palace to see his mother.

After Eumaeus returns, Telemachus leaves, and soon Eumaeus and you, disguised again by Athena as a beggar, proceed to the palace. When you enter the city proper, at the fountain where the townspeople get their water, a goatherd, Melanthius, assaults you and Eumaeus: "Dirt following dirt," he calls you both. He even tries to trip you, but is unsuccessful. Nonetheless, his attempt has angered you. You have a choice to make.

If you choose to indulge your anger and beat Melanthius for his insult, turn to page 79.

If you choose to check your anger and swallow your pride, turn to page 53.

You immediately lash out at Penelope for her insult: "How dare you suggest that someone could move our bed?! I built that bed myself out of an olive tree that grew in the court of the palace. I trimmed it, shaped it, built walls around it, and roofed it. Does the bed remain? Or has someone taken an axe to it?"

Penelope feels her knees go weak. This is the proof she sought. She now knows that her husband has returned. She hugs you and cries. You too cry, overjoyed at not only being home but also being welcomed by your loving wife.

You spend that first night talking, Penelope asking to hear about your travels. Athena even holds the very sun from rising the next morning until you finish talking.

But when the sun finally does rise, you know that you have one final task before you. You summon Telemachus and Eumaeus and strap on your armor.

Continue to the next page.

First, though, you visit your father Laertes. You find him old and stooped in the fields, tending his crops. You test him, at first hiding your identity, but your heart breaks at his anguish, and you quickly reveal yourself. You embrace and return to his house to feast.

In the meantime, the relatives of the killed suitors have taken up arms against you to avenge their dead. You meet outside Laertes' home and begin to fight. But Athena, again disguised as your friend Mentor, appears and urges you to stop fighting and to make peace.

You have a choice to make.

If you choose to ignore Athena and continue fighting, turn to page 107.

If you choose to heed Athena and make peace, turn to page 109.

"Eurymachus, you and your comrades have spent years eating my food, wasting my substance, and insulting my family. But, as your ruler, it is my duty to lead by example. Go home. Leave my palace for good. I will lead you. I will help you when necessary. But I will not be friendly to you or any of the suitors; your prolonged insult has cut too deep."

You turn to join Telemachus and Penelope, ready to rejoin your family. You are so excited that you don't even hear the commotion behind you. Indeed, you don't even hear the clash of metal on metal, sword on shield. What you do hear is Penelope's scream, as she spies the suitors rushing toward you. What you do feel is the piercing pain of swords and the triumphant cheer of the enemy.

You were so close, but for you, this is . . .

THE END

Euryclea, your nurse as a youth, appears, and seeing her brings back floods of memories. But your memories distract you from the impending danger. As she washes your feet, you feel her thumb pass over a scar on your ankle, a scar she knows all too well. Your eyes meet, and you immediately silence her: "Say nothing, old woman. One word to anyone, and I will show you as little mercy as I will show the suitors."

You sleep on the floor that night and awake to the sounds of the arriving suitors. Still they abuse you, one throwing a cow hoof at your head. But you check your rage; you know what awaits them. You just need your opportunity.

Turn to page 78.

"Eurymachus," you begin, "Why should I spare your life? You have been wasting my substance and disrespecting my family. You should be thankful that a quick death will be yours." And with that, you feel the satisfaction of his death.

The battle proceeds. Telemachus fetches your armor and weapons for you when your arrows run out. The treacherous goatherd Melanthius, the one who taunted you on the way to the palace, opened the storeroom where the suitors' armor is stored; they now have armed themselves. You order Eumaeus and his comrade to capture Melanthius and take him away. They do so, but you now have armed suitors to contend with, and you're concerned about the number of them versus the number of you. You have a choice to make.

If you choose to continue the fight, turn to page 73.

If you choose to cut your losses and bargain with the suitors, turn to page 83.

You smile to yourself, but hold your tongue. Your silence indicates your agreement to Penelope's plan.

She speaks, heaviness in her voice: "Stranger, I know not who you are, or how you convinced others that you are my husband, but it is clear that you are not. You may spend the night, but tomorrow you must leave."

Over your protests and the protest of Telemachus, Eumaeus, and Euryclea, Penelope remains silent. You have failed her test. Perhaps eventually you will convince her that it is indeed you, her husband. But you realize that she will never trust you the way she did before.

Whatever the future holds for you and her, you know that your loving marriage and the special bond you shared is lost forever. It may not be the end of your life, but for life as you knew it, it is . . .

THE END

You hear Athena's words, but cannot listen. The pitch of battle has seized you beyond your control. You continue hacking away with your sword, man after man falling before you.

Soon, however, you find your sword arm growing heavy; you are tiring. You find this curious, because mighty Odysseus does not grow tired. But in an instant you realize, tragically, what has happened. Athena is punishing you for ignoring her. So often she helped you on your long and torturous journey home, and now you have ignored her.

You turn, hoping to find her to make peace. But as you turn, you let your guard down, and your enemies pounce. You feel the pain of their swords penetrating your armor. As you fall, you don't know what you regret more, insulting Athena, or letting down your family. Either way, for you, this is . . .

THE END

Your emotions overflow. You embrace Penelope, weeping, before she can even think to stop you. "How dare . . . !" she begins, but she knows. She knows it is you. She pulls you away, holds you at arm's length, gazes in your eyes. Before her, you are transformed; stripped away is your beggar disguise, and resplendent you stand before her. You are both crying, screaming, laughing.

But you are betrayed. Melantho, a devious female servant, hears you and realizes what has happened. Secretly, she steals out of the house and alerts Eurymachus, the suitor who has been her lover, to your presence. He summons Antinous and the other leading suitors.

They surprise you both, asleep, happy, content in bed. The last thing that you notice is that they are not harming Penelope. You are pleased but fear what will happen to her after you are gone. For you know that you will not survive this night.

THE END

Athena's urging brings you happiness. You are weary of fighting and continue it only to defend yourself, your land, and your family. Happily, you lay down your arms as Athena brokers peace between you and the suitors' families.

You see your father back to his house and return to your palace with Telemachus. Penelope waits for you in the doorway. Dinner is prepared, and you sit with her and Telemachus, inviting Eumaeus and Euryclea, your loyal servants, to join you.

Your journey has been long and difficult. You have lost friends and hurt others along the way, but finally have returned home, ready to settle and stay with your loving family, now still mighty Odysseus the warrior, but also mighty Odysseus the husband and father.

Continue to the next page.

CONGRATULATIONS!
YOU HAVE SUCCESSFULLY
FOLLOWED YOUR FATE!

Glossary of Names

Achilles *[ah – KILL – eez]*. Greatest of the Greek warriors whom ODYSSEUS meets in the underworld.

Aegisthus *[aye – GISS – thuss]*. Lover of CLYTEMNESTRA who plotted with her to kill her husband AGAMEMNON upon his return from TROY.

Aeolus *[AYE – oh – lus]*. God of the winds whom ODYSSEUS visits on his journey home.

Agamemnon *[agg – ah – MEM – non]*. Greek general and brother of MENELAUS who led the Greek army against TROY to recover HELEN, the wife of MENELAUS whom PARIS kidnapped.

Ajax *[AY – jacks]*. Great Greek warrior with whom ODYSSEUS contests for the armor of ACHILLES.

Antinous *[An – TIN – oh– us]*. A suitor for the hand of PENELOPE, ODYSSEUS' wife, during ODYSSEUS' absence.

Athena *[ah – THEE – nah]*. Goddess of wisdom, patron goddess of ODYSSEUS, and loyal to the Greeks.

Aulis *[OW – liss]*. A port on the coast north of Athens where the Greek army assembled and from which they departed for TROY and the Trojan War.

Calypso *[kah – LIP – so]*. A goddess whose island ODYSSEUS visits on his journey home.

Charybdis *[kar – IB – dis]*. A sea monster who lives in the narrow strip of water between the northeastern corner of Sicily and the toe of Italy (known today as the Strait of Messina). CHARYBDIS takes the form of a fierce whirlpool that sucks ships into its vortex and is flanked on the other side of the strait by SCYLLA, another voracious monster who eats sailors and ships.

Circe *[SEAR – see]*. A witch with whom ODYSSEUS spends a year of his journey home.

Clytemnestra *[klaye – tem – NESS – trah]*. Wife of AGAMEMNON who killed him upon his return from TROY.

Cyclopes *[Sigh-KLO-peez]*; (**singular = Cyclops** *[SIGH-klops]*). One-eyed monsters made famous by Homer in the *Odyssey* because of the brutish treatment of ODYSSEUS by one of them, named POLYPHEMUS.

Elpenor *[Ell – PEE – nore]*. Companion of ODYSSEUS whom he meets in the underworld.

Eumaeus *[yoo – MAYE – us]*. Swineherd of ODYS-SEUS who lives in ITHACA.

Euryclea *[yur – eh – KLAY – ah]*. Loyal nurse of ODYSSEUS who lives in ITHACA.

Eurylochus *[yur – ILL – uh – cus]*. A companion of ODYSSEUS on his journey home.

Eurymachus *[yur – EH – mock – us]*. One of the suitors of PENELOPE.

Hector *[HECK – tor]*. Greatest of the Trojan warriors, killed by the great Greek warrior ACHILLES, as described in Homer's *Iliad*.

Helen *[HELL – in]*. Wife of the Greek general ME-NELAUS, who was kidnapped by PARIS, and was the cause of the Trojan War.

Helius *[HEE – lee – us]*. God of the sun whose island home ODYSSEUS visits on his journey home.

Hermes *[HER – meez]*. Messenger of the gods, recognized by his winged helmet, winged sandals, and the caduceus, the serpent-entwined staff that is today sometimes used to represent the medical profession.

Ithaca *[ITH – ah – kah]*. Island home of ODYSSEUS, PENELOPE, TELEMACHUS, and LAERTES, off of the northwestern coast of Greece.

Laertes *[lay – AIR – teez]*. Father of ODYSSEUS.

Lastrygonians *[las – trih – GOH – nee – anz]*. A mythological race of cannibalistic giants living on the north coast of the Aegean Sea, whom ODYSSEUS visits on his journey home.

Melanthius *[mel – AN – thee – us]*. A disloyal goatherd who taunts ODYSSEUS upon his return to ITHACA.

Melantho *[mel – AN – tho]*. A female servant in ODYSSEUS' house who is loyal to the suitors.

Mentor *[MEN – tor]*. Friend of ODYSSEUS.

Odysseus *[oh – DISS – ee – us]*. Greek hero and warrior at TROY whose twenty-year journey home is described by Homer in the *Odyssey*.

Palamedes *[pal – ah – MEE – deez]*. Greek sent by AGAMEMNON to convince ODYSSEUS to honor his oath to defend HELEN and to fight in the Trojan War.

Paris *[PAIR – is]*. Trojan prince who, having judged the goddess Aphrodite the most beautiful of the goddesses, was awarded as a prize HELEN, whose kidnapping triggered the Trojan War.

Penelope *[pen – EH – low – pee]*. Wife of ODYSSEUS, who was home in ITHACA awaiting ODYSSEUS' return and resisting the advances of the suitors.

Phaeacians *[faye – EE – shuns]*. The people to whom ODYSSEUS tells his story and whose island is his last stop on his journey home.

Pillars of Hercules *[HER – cue – leez]*. The western border of the Mediterranean, so called because of the narrow strait of water between southern Spain and northern Morocco, and the rock formations that mark it.

Polyphemus *[pol – uh – FEE – mus]*. The CYCLOPS with whom ODYSSEUS interacts on his journey home.

Poseidon *[poh – SIGH – don]*. God of the sea and father of POLYPHEMUS.

Scylla *[SILL – ah]*. A voracious sea monster who lives in the narrow strip of water between the northeastern corner of Sicily and the toe of Italy. SCYLLA eats sailors and ships and is partnered with CHARYBDIS, a whirlpool on the other side of the strait.

Sirens *[SIGH – renz]*. Women perched on a coastal cliff whose song lures sailors to their deaths on the rocks below.

Teiresias *[Tie – REES – ee – us]*. Blind Greek prophet.

Telemachus *[tell – EH – muh – kus]*. Son of ODYSSEUS and PENELOPE.

Troy *[TROY]*. Ancient city located in the northwestern corner of what is today Turkey, which a Greek force led by AGAMEMNON and MENELAUS besieged for ten years and eventually sacked because of the kidnapping of HELEN, the wife of MENELAUS, by the Trojan prince PARIS.

Zeus *[ZOOS]*. King of the gods and god of thunder.

FOLLOW YOUR FATES*
PRESENTS

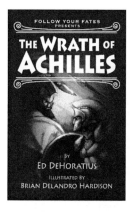

The Wrath of Achilles

By Ed DeHoratius

Illustrated By
Brian Delandro Hardison

x + 62 pp. (2009) 5" x 7¾" Paperback
ISBN 978-0-86516-708-7

You are Achilles, the greatest hero of ancient Greece. You fight with honor and pride.
But on the battlefields of Troy you have a decision to make: stay true to your honor code and
not fight, or stand beside your countrymen
and win even more fame and glory.

In *The Wrath of Achilles*, you face the same choices as Achilles in Homer's
Iliad, but you are in control of your destiny. Only one path leads to glory. Fifteen
others lead to death, defeat, or shame.

Readers ages eight and up will experience Achilles' choices firsthand in Ed
DeHoratius' dramatic text, dynamically illustrated by award-winning comic
book artist Brian Delandro Hardison.

Special Features:

- Prose story of the *Iliad* that puts you right in the action
- 16 different endings—depending on your choices
- 5 illustrations by award-winning comic book artist Brian Delandro
  Hardison
- Visit **http://www.bolchazy.com/followyourfates/** for author podcasts
  and more

Follow Your Fates is a series of books that allows the reader to participate in
the story by making choices that affect the course of the narrative. The reader
assumes the role of the hero-protagonist and makes choices that determine the
hero's responses to the unfolding plot.

In addition to *The Wrath of Achilles* and *The Journey of Odysseus*, the series
includes *The Exile of Aeneas*.

WWW.BOLCHAZY.COM

FOLLOW YOUR FATES*
PRESENTS

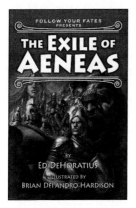

The Exile of Aeneas

By Ed DeHoratius

Illustrated By
  Brian Delandro Hardison

x + 114 pp. (2010) 5" x 7¾" Paperback
ISBN 978-0-86516-709-4

You are Aeneas, Troy's preeminent hero. Your loyalty and integrity are legendary. Will your values hold firm after the destruction of your city, a grueling exile, and yet another war?

In *The Exile of Aeneas*, you face the same decisions as Aeneas in Vergil's *Aeneid*, but you control the outcome. Only one path leads to your destiny. Thirty-one others lead to death, defeat, or shame.

Readers ages eight and up will experience Aeneas' exile and travels first-hand in Ed DeHoratius' dramatic, dynamically illustrated text.

Special Features:

- Prose story of the *Aeneid* that puts you right in the action
- 32 different endings—depending on your choices
- 5 illustrations by award-winning comic book artist Brian Delandro Hardison
- Visit **http://www.bolchazy.com/followyourfates/** for author podcasts and more

Follow Your Fates is a series of books that allows the reader to participate in the story by making choices that affect the course of the narrative. The reader assumes the role of the hero-protagonist and makes choices that determine the hero's responses to the unfolding plot.

In addition to *The Exile of Aeneas* and *The Journey of Odysseus*, the series includes *The Wrath of Achilles*.

www.BOLCHAZY.com